A
COMMUNION
OF SAINTS

Dreams of Happiness on the Road to Life

To Nell & Jamie with love Uncle Dan

Daniel Conway

A
COMMUNION
OF SAINTS

Dreams of Happiness on the Road to Life

Saint Catherine of Siena Press
Indianapolis

© 2011 by Daniel Conway. All rights reserved.

Saint Catherine of Siena Press
4812 North Park Avenue
Indianapolis, IN 46205
888-232-1492
www.saintcathpress.com

To order additional copies of this book:
contact Saint Catherine of Siena Press

Printed in the United States of America.
ISBN-13: 978-0-9800284-4-7

Library of Congress Control Number: 2006920930

Also by Daniel Conway:
    Stewardship in America: A Countercultural Way of Life
    Stewards of Joy
    Advancing the Mission of the Church: Best Practices in Stewardship and Development
        for Catholic Organizations

Front cover design, back cover design, and interior sketches by Mark Castillo.

Back cover photograph of Daniel Conway by Michael Wayne Walker, Portraits of Distinction, Plano, Texas

This book is dedicated to:

David Joseph Champion
Mary Conway Conley
Blaise Hettich, O.S.B.
Anne Bernet O'Donnell
Helen Bernet O'Donnell
Anna May Bernet Callaghan
Dan R. Conway
Joan Callaghan Woodward
G.K. Chesterton* and Charlie Otis**
Thomas M. Rini, Jr.
Thomas J. Murphy
Margaret Nelson Conway
Helen Bernet Callaghan Conway

And all my family and friends,
especially my father, John L. Conway, and
my wife, Sharon Ann Conway, and our children:

Mary Suzanne Conway
Catherine Callaghan Conway
Margaret Ann Conway
Mary Sharon Conway
Daniel Richard Conway

*Gilbert Keith Chesterton (1874-1936) was the author of *The Man Who Was Thursday* (1935) and many other political, social, literary and religious works. His first novel, *The Napoleon of Notting Hill*, which satirized socialism, big business, and technology in his native England, was published in 1904. He converted to Catholicism in 1922 and wrote extensively of his Catholic faith, especially in *Orthodoxy, The Everlasting*

Man, The Catholic Church and Conversion, St. Francis of Assisi, St. Thomas Aquinas and many other books and essays. Chesterton was also a journalist, a mystery writer and a man who loved humor, "the only cure for madness." I trust he will forgive me for the liberties I have taken with his character and his words.

** Charles A. Otis Jr. (1868-1953) was a pioneer in the stock market. He entered the business as a stock broker with Otis, Hough & Co. in 1899, and was the first Clevelander to purchase a seat on the New York Stock Exchange. Helping organize the Cleveland Stock Exchange, he served as its president. He was also referred to as "Mr. Cleveland," because he was president of the Cleveland Chamber of Commerce, now known as the Greater Cleveland Growth Association, was founder of the *Cleveland News* and was a charter member of Cleveland's Union Club. He was a great friend of Timothy J. Conway, my grandfather, and a frequent guest in my grandparents' homes on Claythorne Road and Wetmore Road. He is remembered, among many other things, for his fondness for milk punch.

If, then, you are a pessimist, in reading this story, forgo for a little the pleasures of pessimism. Dream for one mad moment that the grass is green. Unlearn that sinister learning that you think so clear; deny that deadly knowledge that you think you know. Surrender the very flower of your culture; give up the very jewel of your pride; abandon hopelessness, all ye who enter here.

G. K. Chesterton,
Charles Dickens, The Last of the Great Men

"Do not ask of a vision in a dream more than a vision in a dream can give."

"A dream? Then—then—am I not really here, Sir?"

"No, Son," said he kindly, taking my hand in his. "It is not so good as that. The bitter drink of death is still before you. Ye are only dreaming. And if ye come to tell of what ye have seen, make it plain that it was but a dream. See ye make it very plain. Give no poor fool the pretext to think ye are claiming knowledge of what no mortal knows."

C.S. Lewis,
The Great Divorce

In the end, man both needs and longs for just one thing: life, the fullness of life—"happiness." In one passage in John's Gospel, Jesus calls this one simple thing for which we long "perfect joy." (Jn 16:24)

Pope Benedict XVI,
Jesus of Nazareth

Hope springs eternal in the human breast;
Man never Is, but always To be blest:
The soul, uneasy and confin'd from home,
Rests and expatiates in a life to come.

Alexander Pope,
An Essay on Man, Epistle I

Seeing Naples

My mother loved Naples, Florida. It was the site of her geographic cure, the place where she found herself after many lost years. I regret that my mother never knew the original Naples, *Napoli in Italia*. Surely she would have loved it as I do—with its great beauty, its mystery, its resplendent coastline, even its dark and dangerous neighborhoods.

Naples gets under your skin, they say. It insinuates itself into your consciousness and becomes part of you.

Truthfully, Naples is what I imagine death to be, a passageway from life's loneliness and confusion to the peace and being-at-homeness of heaven, an experience of joy that lasts.

"See Naples and die," they say. If this is what my mother experienced in death, then I am truly a son of Naples, *un figlio di Napoli*, more restless here, but also more content and at home than in any other place in my known world.

Daniel Conway
All Souls Day 2008

9

FOREWORD

Nothing is more important than family
by William E. "Uncle Bill" Conway

Dan Conway has written a memoir reflecting on strong women and men, strong memories and strong faith. His conclusion that "nothing is more important than family because family binds us to each other and to God" speaks to an enduring issue in our communities.

I am proud to be a member of Dan's extended family and to share in his dreams.

William E. Conway is Chairman of the Board of Fairmount Minerals, Ltd., an industrial minerals company, headquartered in Chardon, Ohio. A loving husband, father and grandfather, he is the 7th of Margaret and Tim Conway's 13 children and the author's uncle.

11

PREFACE

All of the characters in this little book are real. They are people who influenced me when I was young. Along with many others, living and dead, they helped me discover who I am and what I believe. They are saints—not perfect people, by any means, but good people striving for happiness, the fullness of life. They were, and I trust still are, ordinary women and men seeking the perfect joy that we Christians believe comes at the end of time when this life's journey is ended completely and the Lord comes again to judge the living and the dead.

So, as I say, the characters in this book are real. They remain members of the communion of saints, who intercede for us, and can guide us if we let them, on our journey to heaven.

But these good people are not responsible for the words or actions attributed to them in this book. That is entirely my responsibility, the work of my imagination. I have tried to be faithful to each person, but as I was told by a Benedictine monk many years ago, "Everyone in your dreams is you, or some facet of you." If this is true of actual dreams, it's even truer of imaginary dreams such as these.

There is a danger in using real people, whether living or deceased, to express ideas that are entirely mine. I ask forgiveness, in advance, from anyone who is uneasy about, or offended by, the liberties I have taken here. This is intended to be a love story. I dare to use the family members and friends characterized in these pages because I know from personal experience that they had (and I believe still have) an abundance of love to share.

Still, this is a work of imagination. It is not history or biography or even fiction in the usual sense. I hope it is a work of imagination that is faithful to the Catholic vision of the world—especially to the Church's vision of the mysteries of life and death and resurrection. In addition to being a love story, I intend this to be a story of faith and hope.

All my previous books have been about Christian stewardship: taking care of, and sharing, all God's gifts. This particular book is about the gifts I was given as a young man by the very special people who appear in these pages. I owe them much gratitude and respect. And with these pages I hope to pass on to others something of the faith, hope and love they shared with me when I was a young man. I was hurt, angry and confused, and they showed me how to be reasonably happy and at peace. I was lonely and afraid, and they reached out to me and loved me.

May God bless them—every one.

Daniel Conway
August 2009

CHAPTER 1
A detour on the road to life

I am in a coma. I can see and hear, but I can't speak or move or communicate in any way. The effort is exhausting. I know what's going on around me, but I'm cut off from everyone. I feel really alone and hopeless.

I don't know how long I've been here—in this hospital. I'm awake for a little while, probably no more than 10 or 20 minutes, and then I relapse into a kind of sleep. I think I'm sleeping, but the dreams I'm having are much more vivid, and coherent, than in my usual sleep. In fact, when I'm dreaming now, all of my senses are on high alert. I see, hear, taste, smell and touch with great sensitivity.

I can smell the face powder my Grandmother Callaghan used to wear. I hear my mother's smoker's cough distinctly although I know she died more than 10 years ago. Sweet corn and fried tomatoes excite my taste buds the way they did 45 years ago during summer vacations at the Conway Farm. And the cool waves of the Atlantic Ocean soothe my sunburned arms and shoulders just as they did many years ago when I was a small child on vacation with my family in Ft. Lauderdale.

Sensations from a long, long time ago come back to me now that I am barely alive. Accompanying these vivid sense experiences are perfectly clear and detailed images of the places I knew in my childhood. But they're not just images. I am actually here—in all these places—the old Callaghan place on County Line Road on the outskirts of Cleveland, Ohio; at our parish, the Church of the Gesu, across the street from John Carroll University; on the beach at 4th Avenue North in Naples, Florida; in the monastic cemetery at Saint Meinrad Archabbey in southern Indiana; and in many other places from my past.

Strangely, I am not an outsider, or just a visitor from long ago. I am truly at home in all these wondrous places. Much more at home, in fact, than when I was young. In those days, these were strange new places full

17

of mystery and adventure but also of pain and anxiety. Now they are all part of me, integral to who I am, for better or worse.

How odd it seems to experience so intensely places that until the accident were just distant memories, sometimes happy and sometimes sad, but mainly remote recollections from an increasingly distant past. As I grew older, these childhood places seemed to fade further and further away, and I remembered them only as the remote scenery or background spaces for my growing up in the suburbs of Cleveland, in southern Indiana, and in Naples, Florida.

But not now. Now they are alive again. I am in the barn where we saddled the horses, and the smells overwhelm me. I am in the sunroom where my grandmother's chair is, and I can feel the sun's rays warming my entire body. I am sitting in Corky and Lenny's Delicatessen with all its pungent smells and the clamor of plates and people. These are wonderful places. They are alive again in totally new ways, and I am happy to be here—one last time?

I don't remember much about the accident. I was driving home on Blankenbaker Lane, a narrow and winding road in an area of Louisville, Kentucky, that was once the plantation home of George Rogers Clark. It was raining, and very dark, and the road was slippery. I was distracted, thinking about my job, how I really want a change from the stresses of the past 10 years. "I'm 60 years old," I was thinking, "and I may only have 10 years left to work. It's time to do something different."

Then I saw a deer—the first of two of them—running across the road. I was able to swerve and miss the first one, but the second deer was a dead hit. I remember the sudden impact, the car spinning out of control and the immediate, paralyzing fear. I hit my head on the steering wheel just as the airbag exploded. After that, nothing ... until I woke up in this hospital room unable to move or speak, and I began lapsing in and out of consciousness, experiencing the most powerful dreams I have ever had.

The places in my dreams are amazing, but they're nothing compared to the people. Each time I fall into a dream-like state, I encounter someone from my past who has died. I've dreamed about dead people before, but never like this. Now I'm having real conversations, about things that matter to me, with people I knew and loved many years ago. 1 people who were very important to me but who have been gor long time—some for all of my adult life.

I honestly don't know why I'm having these dreams. (Could it be the drugs they're giving me?) I could be losing my mind, traumatized by the accident, but truthfully I don't care what's causing this. The opportunity to be with so many people that I loved and lost so many years ago is thrilling. It's a true-to-life fantasy, a dream come true and a gift I never expected. Does that make me weird—to want to reconnect with people who are dead? Most people want nothing to do with death. We don't talk about it. We treat it superficially or pretend that it's no big deal ("just another stage of life"). But, of course, death is a very big deal—the end of life as we know it, a violent change in our existence and a total disconnection with the everyday world and the people we interact with, and care about, here and now.

I've always believed in some kind of life after death. My Grandmother Callaghan died suddenly when I was 15, and it hit me really hard. I didn't want to lose her. I believed then that the people we love and lose in death remain vital and present—in some way—in spite of all evidence to the contrary. But that was an abstract belief, not a vivid personal experience like this. I have also always taken seriously the Church's conviction, which I eventually made my own, that Christ has conquered death, so that when we die we are with Christ in some mysterious way until the Last Day when we will all rise again. I say I have always believed this, but never until now did I have any inkling of what all this might mean, concretely, for me or for the people I love.

My mother died 10 years ago after a prolonged illness that she tried, unsuccessfully, to hide from us. Since then, I have hoped—with all the certainty of faith in Christ—that we would be together again one day and that her indomitable spirit would endure long after she slipped away from us in a hospital bed very much like the one I am in now. But how could I know for sure? What was clear, beyond any doubt, was the fact that the complex living person who gave me life and who was the source of so much pain and confusion, but also joy and inspiration, for nearly 50 years, was no longer alive. We buried the body that was no longer her following a wonderful Mass and a lengthy funeral procession through the streets of Naples, Florida. My mother is dead—really dead—just like all the other family members and friends who are visiting me now in these dreams. And yet I believe that love is stronger than death, and that my mother, and all the saints who have died, live—really and truly—in Christ.

Why doesn't it frighten me to see these dear people from my distant past alive again? I really don't know. Perhaps it's because they are so real. They're not ghosts, and they're certainly not intimidating. In fact, they are just as they always were—only more so. What I mean is, the qualities that attracted me to these long-dead friends and family members are all I notice now. Of course, they all had faults, prejudices, idiosyncrasies and lots of problems. These don't bother me now. I only see the love and friendship that made them so special to me—in spite of whatever else was going on in their lives or mine.

I don't know why I'm having these dreams or why I'm revisiting these special places from my childhood or why I'm being united with people who have not been part of my daily life for a very long time. Does this mean that I'm dying? That my life is passing before my eyes in one or more of my final moments? Perhaps. But, then, why don't these important last moments also involve the people whom I love who are still alive—my wife, Sharon, and our five children, my 87-year-old father, my sisters and brothers, my good friends and my large, extended family? Surely they would also be visible to me during a final deathbed review of my 60 years of life.

The fact is I'm not ready to die. I have too much left to do—personally, professionally and, most of all, spiritually. So, I don't know why the dead are visiting me now. But I've decided I'm not going to worry about it. I'm too fascinated by the chance to be with these very special people who I never thought I'd see again—at least in this life. If nothing else, I want to thank each one of them for the gifts they gave me. I want to tell them all—one last time—how much I love them, each in a different way, and how much I miss them every day of my life.

CHAPTER 2
DJ

We are sitting on cold hard metal chairs in a church basement. It's the parish church of our childhood, but it could be any church basement anywhere. DJ is next to me. He looks like he did 30 years ago when we both had young families. I always envied the way DJ looked. He was thin and handsome with sandy hair and a captivating smile. The guys we hung out with in high school used to tease him because of his Dobie Gillis look, but somehow DJ could get away with wearing "preppy" clothes that would have made the rest of us feel completely out of place.

DJ had girlfriends before most of us did. He also had "girl troubles" that caused the rest of us to wonder if being a ladies' man was really worth it. Still, every one of my high school friends would have gladly traded his lonely bachelor status for some of DJ's "action." In college, most of them did.

The last time DJ and I were in this church basement was during our senior year of high school. (I think we're sitting on the same chairs—42 years later—and they haven't gotten any softer!) We were active in our parish youth group, the Gesu Juniors, and we attended dances and other youth activities here, including committee meetings that mainly served as an excuse to get out of the house on Sunday nights.

But none of this explains why DJ and I are here now. He died 8 years ago following the total failure of his lungs due to damage caused by heavy smoking. Doctors at the Cleveland Clinic succeeded in giving him a lung transplant, but they couldn't control the infections that developed afterwards. DJ died at 52, leaving a wonderful wife, Sandy, and three sons who now have families of their own.

I'm relieved that DJ speaks to me first. I'm not sure what to say to him—beyond the fact that I've really missed him and I hope he's OK (now that he's dead!).

23

"You don't appreciate the important things until you lose them," he says, pontificating the way he always did when he thought he had something especially worthwhile to say. "I always knew that Sandy was special, and I definitely could not have made it through the last years without her, but I took her for granted for too long."

He doesn't sound sad or sentimental, but there's no doubt that he misses her. DJ used to say that he dated lots of pretty girls, but he married a beautiful woman, a partner who could share his life and help him become a better man. He always said that marrying Sandy was the smartest thing he ever did.

"You should pay more attention to Sharon," he tells me. "There will come a time when you'll find yourself longing to touch her again, to run your fingers through her hair and kiss her. Sex doesn't die when we do," he tells me, becoming visibly excited, his voice rising in pitch. "The desire remains—stronger than ever—to be united physically as well as in mind and heart. Sandy and I will always be one in spirit, but the flesh is important too. I honestly didn't realize how lucky I was, in so many ways, to be loved by a feisty, strong-willed redhead like Sandy."

When DJ and Sandy first met, he had just broken up with a girlfriend and he had sworn off women for six months. Sandy bet him $20 he couldn't do it. When his roommates found out, they howled with laughter and advised Sandy that she would have to follow him around all weekend in order to make sure he kept his side of the bargain. In the end, DJ lost the bet but won Sandy.

In fact, he never got over his love for women. Sandy's friends all loved him. He flirted with them constantly and could always find something uniquely special in each of them. It was the same with the women he worked with. He was always respectful, and genuine in his affection, and he complimented them often—praising the sparkle in Suzy's eyes or the warmth in Janie's beautiful smile. He had a gift that both men and women recognized. He could make you feel like you were the only person in the world. Even when he was suffering, and in danger of losing hope, he managed to make the hospital staff at the Cleveland Clinic smile and feel better about themselves in spite of the losing battle they were waging on his behalf.

During the final days of his life, Sandy told him that Tibetan monks laugh every day before they get out of bed. DJ and Sandy decided they would do the same. Some days they had a hard time finding something to laugh about. But they did it—every day!

DJ leans back on his folding chair. It's a wonder it doesn't collapse. He is quiet for several minutes. I assume he's thinking about Sandy. It's never occurred to me that dead men think about sex—intimate physical contact, or communion—the way we who are living do. I know that love changes over the years. Sharon and I have been married for 30 years, and there's no question that our love is different now. I believe it's deeper and stronger than ever, but it's also more familiar and comfortable. DJ is right. I should pay more attention to Sharon. I should also find something to laugh about every day!

I find I can't hold back any longer. Taking advantage of his silence, I ask—way too bluntly, "What was it like to die? And what's it like now? And what do have to look forward to when we die? Is there really something better to come?"

DJ responds, with a gentleness that is comforting, "Man, I can't describe death to you. There's no way you would understand it. You have to go through it yourself. And what it's like for me now isn't really important. What matters is the way you live your life—however long you've got left."

I feel like an idiot, like I somehow invaded his personal space.

"Don't be silly," he says. "I'd be asking the same questions if I were in your place, but there are some things that can only be understood by experiencing them. Death is life's greatest mystery. While we're alive, we are right to hope for a better life to come, but we have no way of knowing for sure. The only way to prepare for death, to embrace its secrets, is by living well."

"OK, thanks," I say, still feeling embarrassed and uncomfortable. "So, how should I prepare for death? Is it happening to me now? Will I have to suffer the way you did?"

DJ smiles. "You're getting ahead of yourself. Live from one moment to the next, one day at a time, without worrying about the future. Here we are together again, for the first time in 8 years, and all you can think about is what may happen to you at the end of your life. That ending could be 20 minutes, or 20 years, from now!

"And as for suffering, it will come to you in ways that are unique to you—mental, physical or emotional. Each person has to follow his own path in order to safely pass through the violence and uncertainty of death. When we were kids—here at Gesu school—we were taught that the sufferings of Christ opened the way for us. We were also taught to "offer up" our suffering for the benefit of others (including the poor souls in purgatory). For most of my adult life, I didn't think about any of this. But when my lungs gave out and I had to face the bitter realities of suffering and death, whether I wanted to or not, the truths the Sisters taught us began to make sense.

"We can't avoid death," he says. "But it's a big mistake to dwell on it. You need to accept every moment of your life as the gift that it is. As long as you still have breath within you, you are incredibly blessed. Choose life—even when it means you must suffer. There's no such thing as a life that's not worth living. With all its pain, its loneliness, its fear and its anger, life is a gift from God. Embrace it, and don't look back. Above all, don't feel sorry for yourself. There's no future in it."

"I'm sorry, DJ. You're right. It's just a lot to deal with—the accident, these dreams and all of you ... ." I stop myself before saying "ghosts" because I know that can't be right.

"By the way, what are you exactly? I know you're not alive any more, but I don't think you're a ghost or a spirit. What should I call you?"

"Why don't you just call me your friend?"

"Fair enough," I say, once again feeling foolish. "You were always a good friend to me, and I've missed you."

To tell the truth, I'm eager to change the subject. Things have gotten way too heavy.

"Why are we here in the Gesu Parish Hall?" I ask.

"There's an AA meeting tonight, and I haven't been to one in 8 years," DJ says. "AA changed my life, you know. I let booze take the place of spiritual growth, and I really suffered for it. So did my family. I abused my body, but also my mind and my soul, by years of excessive smoking and drinking," he says looking grim for the first time in our conversation.

At DJ's funeral, his younger brother, Tom, talked about how AA had changed his brother's life. After many years of heavy drinking and smoking, he had lost all sense of faith or spirituality. He had to be dragged to Mass on Christmas. He was bitter and resentful about the way his life had turned out. But once he found sobriety and got active in AA, his attitude was very different. He was grateful and at peace—in spite of his suffering and disappointments.

"Alcoholics Anonymous uses the basic principles of spirituality that are found in most of the world's great religions and applies them to daily living," he says. "What we were looking for in the bottle, we find gradually, and more authentically, by working the 12 steps and living the AA principles as best we can—one day at a time.

"Do you know what surprised me the most when I first started to attend AA meetings?"(It's obviously a rhetorical question—he's pontificating again—so I don't try to respond.)

"Laughter. Here we are—a bunch of drunks who've made a real mess of our lives. But instead of feeling sorry for ourselves, or moping around like a bunch of Sad Sacks, we enjoy life. We're grateful for all our blessings, and we do our best to repair the wreckage of our past not by focusing on it, but by looking forward in love."

I can see that the meeting is about to start. The room is filling up with people—mostly middle aged or older but some much younger too—and from every race, ethnic group and social status. I don't recognize anyone, but they all look familiar. I know this is just a dream, but I feel an incredible sense of belonging. These are my kind of people— spiritual seekers who had lost their way but now are "looking forward in love."

DJ smiles again. "I missed you, man."

"Me, too, friend."

✳ ✳ ✳

I open my eyes and see Sharon sitting in a chair beside my bed. How many days and nights has she been here?

There's no doubt that Sharon is the best thing that happened to me. I met her when I was teaching theology at St. Ignatius High School in Cleveland. (I taught 3 of her 8 brothers.) When I first saw Sharon at one of our high school basketball games, I was "blown away." She was so beautiful, and so completely self-possessed, that I said to myself "if she's as nice as her brothers, I have to meet her." I asked the boys to introduce me to her the following weekend, and she agreed to go out with me—mainly to placate her brothers who had become my advocates. For me, it was love at first sight, but Sharon was more discriminating. We dated briefly, got engaged and married less than a year later.

As our married life has unfolded, I've come to recognize what a gift she is to me. It hasn't always been easy, of course, but our more than 30 years together have been a real blessing. They've taught me that Sharon is every bit the strong-willed and independent woman I fell in love with three decades ago. But I also know now that she can be anxious, and quite vulnerable, especially when life doesn't go as planned.

She is sitting here now being strong for me and for our children. If only I could touch her, and let her know that all is well with me. Especially now, I wish I could tell her that I'm OK. That I'm getting better. That I will love her, and be with her, for many more years. I scream silently, "I love you—forever!"

DJ would say that I'm getting ahead of myself. That I need to let go, to surrender, and trust in God. But letting go is so hard … .

Talking to DJ has really worn me out. I'm exhausted. At least I can sleep.

CHAPTER 3
Aunt Mary

It's a cool summer evening, and I am with Aunt Mary in the pavilion of the Blossom Music Center, the summer home of the Cleveland Orchestra. Blossom Center is in the Cuyahoga River Valley of northeast Ohio, roughly halfway between the industrial cities of Cleveland and Akron. It's a perfect setting for summer concerts. The gently sloping hills and lush valleys make this an especially peaceful place—far removed physically and spiritually from the noise and congestion of its urban neighbors.

The Conway Farm was just a couple of miles from here. My grandfather bought it during the Great Depression as a summer home for his very large family. I spent many summers at the farm with my parents, my brothers and sisters, my grandfather, and my many aunts, uncles and cousins.

Aunt Mary, my father's older sister, brought me here to Blossom Center many years ago to attend my first ballet. I was 13, and I was not at all interested in ballet, but I would have gone anywhere with Aunt Mary. She always made me feel special. She talked to me as an adult, and she asked perceptive questions and then listened intently to my answers. When I was with Aunt Mary, I wasn't 13. I was as grown up and mature as she was, a companion she treated with great love and respect.

I was always comfortable being with Aunt Mary, and that sense of ease carries over to this dream. I'm not surprised to see her, and I'm not the least bit embarrassed or uncomfortable being with her again after nearly 25 years. She is a beautiful woman, a gracious and refined lady, with a gentle and affirming smile. All her life she struggled to keep her weight down—sometimes successfully, often not. When I was young, she told me I would engage in a similar lifelong battle. I didn't want to hear it then, but I knew she was right. Now, she looks wonderful. Her skin is clear and smooth, and the slight gray in her hair makes her seem mature but not elderly.

"Tell me about yourself, dear," she says, "and about your family. I know your children are all grown now. Tell me how they're doing."

This would be a nonconversation with almost anyone else. I'd say the children are fine, or allude in a very general way to the fact that they are now experiencing "the challenges of adult living" and quickly move on to something else. But I know that Aunt Mary understands the strange mix of joy and sorrow that is involved in watching your adult children make their own choices and experience their own successes and failures.

So I tell her how I feel—proud, frustrated, hopeful, afraid and sometimes angry (at myself and them)—all mixed together with great love and anticipation.

Aunt Mary listens carefully and then says, "We can't help making mistakes with our children. There's no instruction manual or recipe book for rearing children, and even if there were, we'd misread it or unintentionally leave out some essential ingredient."

She gives me her knowing smile, which is reassuring but which also invites me to share in her own sadness. Aunt Mary always carried her sadness well. She didn't brood or pout, and she was determined to put the best possible face on everything. But there was always a hint of melancholy, just beneath the surface, even in her happiest and most peaceful moments. Aunt Mary expected the very best from life, and as a result she was always at least slightly disappointed. Fortunately, that didn't prevent her from enjoying life. (What fun times we had as children with Aunt Mary and her family!)

"Children reflect the best and the worst qualities of their parents," she says, no doubt thinking about her own children and grandchildren. "But they are not simply carbon copies of us. They make their own way in the world—for better or worse—and no matter how much we'd like to determine the results of their choices, we can only pray that God's love will guide and sustain them."

"Did you ever wish you could go back and start over," I ask. I'm suddenly aware of all the ways that I failed as a husband and father during the past three decades.

"Of course. We begin our adult lives with great expectations, but we quickly learn that suffering and disappointment—in many different forms—will be our daily companions. That's why it's so important for us to keep our double chins up," she says referring to the infamous Conway double chin and smiling again, this time without any hint of sadness.

"I know that," I say. "There's no point in feeling sorry for myself. For one thing, I've been really blessed—far outweighing all my problems as a child and as an adult. And, I know from experience that focusing on problems only makes them worse!"

"You're exactly right, dear. The secret to happiness is acceptance. Not passivity or false humility, but the kind of active acceptance that requires courage and the determination to make the best of every bad situation, trusting that, in the end, God will provide all that we need to make the right choices."

"I know you're right, Aunt Mary. That's the way my father has lived his whole life. I wish I could be more like him, but it's really tough. My mother learned to surrender the hard way, and it saved her life, so I'm absolutely convinced that what you say is true—that it's the secret to happiness. I believe it intellectually. I just can't seem to live it very well."

She is quiet for what seems like a long time, and I recognize the far away look that used to come over her when she was worried. As a young man, I learned to respect those moments and to wait until Aunt Mary returned from whatever remote section of her expansive heart she was currently occupying.

"Just because I'm no longer alive doesn't mean that I'm free from all my worries." She speaks to me as though I have been following her thoughts, sensing her anxiety. "That day will come, but as long as time continues we who are dead remain engaged with the people we love. We pray for you. We rejoice with you, and we also share in your troubles. We don't worry about the final outcome of your lives. We have too much confidence in God's mercy. But just as it did when you were little children, it hurts us to see you stumble and fall—especially knowing that there is nothing we can do to shield you from the consequences of your own actions and decisions."

"Knowing that you still love us is a great comfort, Aunt Mary. "It's a shame that we so easily forget about those who have died. I guess that's why as children we were taught to pray for the dead and to have confidence that our prayers would make a difference. Today we assume that family members and friends who die either go straight to heaven (whatever that means) or go nowhere. We rarely think of you as somehow present, involved in our lives in any real way."

The orchestra is warming-up and the pavilion is now full of people. On the lawn surrounding us people have been spreading blankets and opening their picnic baskets.

"What are we going to hear," I ask. (I hope it's not another ballet.)

"Mozart," Aunt Mary tells me. "And some rarely performed chamber music by Paisello. It's been such a long time since I went to a concert. I can hardly wait!"

"You were always a fan of great art and music," I say. "What happens to our passion for the arts when we die?"

"Our desire for beauty is part of our search for the meaning of life. We don't leave it behind when we die. In fact, it intensifies as we are freed from the distractions of earthly life. The quest for authentic spirituality that begins while we are living continues beyond the grave. If we are true to ourselves, and to the God whose love draws us forward, we will find complete beauty and truth (the ultimate happiness) on the Last Day."

I have the strongest desire to tell Aunt Mary how much I love her. And how much her spiritual journey has always meant to me. But before I can speak, the conductor signals that it is time to begin. It is the overture to Mozart's first mature opera, *Idomeneo*, a story about conflicted men and women trying to placate a capricious god. I am carried away by the passion of this gifted young composer, and I really hope that I'll get to hear all this sublime music before I wake up from this dream.

✷ ✷ ✷

Dr. Tom Blanford, who is my internist and also my neighbor, is leaning over me, shining a light in my eyes and waving his finger at me. Tom is the most humble and unassuming physician I've ever met. He's also the only person I've ever known who plays classical music on an accordion!

I hear him talking to Sharon. Apparently the accident caused severe trauma to my brain. No one seems to know when, or if, I will recover. "We hope it's not permanent," he tells her, "but we don't know for sure." I appreciate his directness, but this is not encouraging news.

My children are here with Sharon. I'm happy to see them, but I don't want to burden them. I want to reach out to them, and hug them, but of course I can't move.

My mother always said of us, her seven children, that we were all alike but each one was different. The same is true of my five kids. To the casual observer, they look and act the same, but on closer inspection each one is nothing like the others. In a way, they are mirror images of Sharon and me—like us in every way only different!

Children reflect the best and the worst qualities of their parents, Aunt Mary said. Sharon and I have given our children our strong wills and our independence. May God grant them the serenity to accept the things they cannot change, the courage to change the things they can, and the wisdom to know the difference.

Sleep comes again, a welcome relief but also a threat. I really don't want to die.

CHAPTER 4
Father Blaise

The monastic cemetery at Saint Meinrad Archabbey is a place of simplicity and symmetry. Unlike most graveyards, its headstones are all uniform, the same sandstone crosses lined up in rows (not unlike the white wooden crosses you see in national cemeteries). There's something comforting about the order and consistency of this holy place. Whenever I return to Saint Meinrad, I try to get down to the cemetery to make a visit.

Because my association with Saint Meinrad goes back more than 40 years, I knew a lot of the monks who are buried in this cemetery. Many of them taught me in college or in the graduate school of theology. Some were good friends, mentors or spiritual directors who helped me make the Catholic faith something that I can call my own. I have never claimed to be a particularly good Christian, but my years at Saint Meinrad helped me develop an adult faith that I take quite seriously.

On the far side of the cemetery, opposite from where all my former teachers and confrères are buried, I see Father Blaise, a thin and wiry middle-aged monk wearing the long black habit and cowl that identify him as a member of the Benedictine order. He is doing "rubbings" on the headstones of monks I never knew, men who died long before I first came to Saint Meinrad as a college freshman in 1967. He also seems to be talking to himself, and laughing out loud, with the booming bass voice that we students loved to imitate. "Ho, ho, ho," we would loudly proclaim, not quite getting it right. "I have a doctorate in English literature. I teach poetry and linguistics and Shakespeare," we'd continue, mimicking his distinctive bravado. "I don't suffer fools gladly, and I certainly don't have the time, or the patience, to read papers that are poorly written!"

We made fun of him, but we respected him. He shared with us his passion for great writing and for the power of poetic imagery to bring life to humanity's joys and sorrows; and he was always available for formal counseling or just to talk. His untimely death as a man in his 50s was a great shock to all of us. Although he was always frail and had been sickly as a young man, we had no idea that his heart would fail him in this way.

"Better to reign in hell than be ruled in heaven," he says, quoting Milton's Lucifer from *Paradise Lost*. "Old Milton got that one exactly right. We would rather do it our way and be damned than surrender to God's will and attain happiness. I struggled with that every day in the monastery. St. Benedict's rule, his program for monastic living, is designed to help us confront our selfishness and learn to live as God intended. I tried to be a faithful monk," he says, "but my pride and my self-centeredness kept getting in the way. I now know that purgatory is monastic life on steroids; it's the radical stripping away of our willful self-contradictions."

"Are you in purgatory now, Father?" I ask timidly. I don't want to offend him, but he's the one who brought it up, and I'm more than a little curious.

He dismisses my question with a wave of his hand and utters a kind of "tut, tut" sound that lets me know I have missed the point. "Purgatory is not a place where sinners are sent to be tortured as a punishment for their sins," he says in a loud voice with great emphasis. "It's the continuation of a conversion process that has to begin, consciously or not, while we're still alive. What actually saves us is the unqualified "Yes!" that every individual person is asked to say in response to God's invitation to give ourselves to Him alone. But most of us hold back. Our yeses are tentative and conditional. We can't quite bring ourselves to say yes to God wholeheartedly.

"God's love is unconditional," Father Blaise assures me. "But before we can open our hearts to accept him, we have to be transformed. Purgation, the purifying fire, is not a punishment; it is a gift that helps us ready ourselves for the encounter with Christ, the source of lasting joy. We first receive this gift at the time of our baptism, and it is renewed every time we receive the sacrament of penance. And, except for those who die in an exceptional state of self-sacrificing love, this essential process of transformation must continue beyond death until we are capable of being united with God forever in heaven."

Father Blaise always prided himself on his brief and straightforward approach to religion and spirituality. His homilies were never more than 7 minutes long, and he almost always limited himself to two or three simple, but always insightful, ideas that he called "reflection starters." The ideas he just shared with me about conversion and repentance continuing after death aren't simple, but they certainly qualify as reflection starters!

"What's your favorite play by Shakespeare?" he asks. I'd be completely thrown off by this sudden change of topic if I didn't know that Father Blaise is just trying to make a point.

"Macbeth."

"I'm not surprised. What is it about *Macbeth* that interests you more than the other plays?"

I've never given this much thought. "I suppose it's the directness and the intensity of the passions that Macbeth and his Lady represent. Every emotion is fierce and unrestrained, and the entire play moves swiftly to its inevitable conclusion. I've always been fascinated by the way Shakespeare handles the interaction between the living and the dead. The witches and the spirits they invoke operate in a kind of twilight zone that is both in this world and beyond it."

"True enough," he says. "But what does that tell you about human experience, about the so-called 'real world' that ordinary people live in day-in and day-out?"

I have to think about this. I just saw a performance of *Macbeth* in Chicago a couple of months ago with my cousin Ann. We talked about it afterwards, and I remember saying that the Macbeths' ambitions were a perversion of their most basic and natural desires. They want to be gods, suprahuman beings who are in absolute control. Anyone who stands in their way—or has the potential to be in the way—must be removed at all costs. And all the natural (and supernatural) forces in the universe must be subjected to their wills in order to satisfy their insatiable lust for power.

"It tells me that we ordinary men and women regularly delude ourselves into thinking we're in control when clearly we are not. Everything in *Macbeth* is exaggerated for dramatic purposes, but everything in the play is as real and 'ordinary' as life itself. We all spend far too much time trying to remake the world according to our own specifications. The result is always a disappointment—and sometimes a disaster."

Father Blaise is thinking. He's wrapped himself in the dark folds of his Benedictine habit with his hood up, which probably means he's cold. I don't know what time of year it is, but it feels like February. The night air is damp and the temperature has been falling. I know this is just a dream, but I'm beginning to think it's not such a good idea to be here in the cemetery at nighttime.

"Nonsense!" he bellows, once again waiving his hand at me dismissively. Has he sensed my childish fear of being here late at night, or is he being critical of my interpretation of *Macbeth?*

I'm afraid I'll never know. I'm surrounded by bright lights, and I'm being placed into a tunnel-like machine. I'm disoriented by the abrupt change of scenery. Apparently I've been moved to another part of hospital for a CAT scan, an MRI or some other exotic test. I wish I knew what Father Blaise thinks is nonsense. And I sure wish I knew what was happening to me now.

CHAPTER 5
The Bernet Women

On the other side of the tunnel, it seems, is the old Callaghan place on County Line Road. I'm in the living room watching television, Saturday morning cartoons, just as I did when I was little. I would get up early and watch all my favorite shows until my grandmother came and told me to go outside and play. Luckily she always slept late!

Going outside was not something I did unwillingly. There were lots of wonderful old trees for me to climb, and plenty of woods and open fields to explore. I never minded being alone at Grandma's place. I could occupy myself for hours pretending to be whomever I wanted to be—a pirate, a superhero or sometimes just a grownup man free to do whatever I wanted.

I can hear voices down the hallway through the dining room and into the sunroom where the adults always gathered. My grandmother, Anna May Bernet Callaghan, is visiting with her sister, Helen Bernet O'Donnell, whom we called "Huno." (When he was a little boy, my Uncle Jack Callaghan couldn't say "Helen," so it was Huno evermore!) With them is Huno's daughter, Anne Bernet O'Donnell, who died just two months ago at the age of 72. Grandma has been gone for a very long time—since 1964. Huno lived longer, but, even so, she has been dead for 30 years.

The house is unforgettable. The main section was an old barn that my grandmother moved to this site and then converted. It had majestic wooden beams and original hardwood floors. The kitchen, bedrooms and bathrooms were added-on as was the sunroom. Beneath the house were two separate cellars filled with old furniture and boxes of old clothes. There was an attic, too, that you reached by climbing an old wooden staircase. The attic was a place of musty mystery. When the weather was bad, and the Saturday morning cartoons were over, you could spend many hours exploring the attic.

"Hello, Dan." (It's Annie O'Donnell, my mother's cousin.) "I didn't think we'd see each other again so soon." We taught together at St. Ignatius High School in Cleveland in the late 1970s, but for the past 30 years we've only seen each other occasionally—mainly at weddings and funerals.

"Your funeral was incredible," I say. "The church was filled to overflowing with all the people whose lives you touched as a teacher, a counselor and a friend. You really are missed."

"I probably would have done it differently," she says, "but you can't tell the Jesuits anything. They have to do it their way."

Five Jesuits and two diocesan priests were at the altar during Anne's funeral. Since she had no immediate family left, her many cousins and hundreds of friends bid her a heartfelt farewell. The homily, which was two-parts personal reminiscence and one-part reflection on Sacred Scripture, had everyone alternating between laughter and tears. Anne was stubborn and opinionated and old-fashioned, Father said. But she cared deeply about her faith, her family and her students. She truly made a difference in the world through her dedication to others.

During the eulogy before Mass, one of Anne's former students, now a middle-aged man, told about the time he wrecked his father's car and didn't have enough money to pay for the repairs. Miss O'D, as he called her, lent him the money, but she struck a tough bargain in return. He had to go with her to the 6 a.m. daily Mass at Gesu for a month—no excuses allowed. Heads were nodding throughout the church. This was obviously not the only time she struck such a deal with one of her students.

"I had two choices," she says looking at me with a Master Teacher's gaze, the look that rivets a student to his chair and demands absolute attention. "I could feel sorry for myself and be lonely, or I could reach out to others and make them part of my family. I decided I had no use for fools—for people who only care about themselves. Love and service are the meaning of life, the only way to be really happy."

"What's it like now?" I ask. "Is life after death boring?"

"Are you kidding? Give me a break. I've got more work to do than ever. When you dedicate your life to serving others, the opportunities to be fulfilled are endless. And, besides, keeping an eye out for the Jesuits is a full-time job. They're always on the verge of screwing up something."

I can see Huno coming down the hallway. She is a large woman, unlike my grandmother who is very frail, and she wears her graying hair in a bun.

"Anne, dear, we must be going. Your father and brother are waiting for us at the club."

Even a quarter of a century later, Huno is a legend at the Shaker Heights Country Club. Every Sunday night, without fail, the O'Donnell family went to the club for dinner. And when they arrived, every waiter, cook, busboy and club employee would line up as Huno passed by to greet Mrs. O'Donnell personally and to receive from her a generous tip.

"I'm coming, Mother. Dan and I were just talking about my funeral Mass. He was there, you know, along with so many of our family members and friends."

"I always thought that church was too big and too modern," Huno says referring to the "new" Gesu Church, which was built in 1959 in anticipation of the liturgical renewal that followed Vatican II. (Huno prefers an older style of church architecture, one that emphasizes the mysterious dimensions of faith and worship.) "But I have to admit that it looked especially lovely the day they laid you to rest. And such beautiful music!

"We really have to run along now, Dan," Huno says as she wraps herself in an ancient wool coat and a cashmere scarf that are too heavy for this time of year. "Go in and spend some time with your grandmother. She's looking forward to having dinner with you."

I watch as Huno and Anne head out to the car. Like my grandmother, my Aunt Joan, and my mother, they are incredibly strong women. Stubborn, opinionated and old-fashioned, just like Father said in his homily. All my life, I have been fascinated by them, the daughters and granddaughters of John J. Bernet, a Cleveland railroad executive who was called "the doctor of sick railroads." All my life, I have been drawn to them, to their intelligence, to their iron-willed determination and to the air of mystery (and tragedy) that surrounds them.

I walk slowly down the hallway toward the sunroom. I'm trembling with anticipation. My grandmother's death was the most intense experience of my young life. At just 15, I was totally unprepared for the violent emotions that swept over me. I had never known such loneliness. I was inconsolable. Only Aunt Joan, my mother's sister, appeared to recognize the extent of my pain. She cried with me, sensing that there were no words that would make any difference. How I loved her for sharing my grief that way—and for all the kind and thoughtful things she did for me when I was growing up. Years later, I cried those very same bitter and lonely tears when my mother told me that Aunt Joan had died.

Grandma is in the sunroom sitting in her chair by the door. I bend down and kiss her on the cheek, but there is nothing I can say. I nearly choke just trying to say hello.

"Come in, dear. We're having Stouffer's Lobster Newburg and toast for dinner, just the way you like it. But be sure to save room for an ice cream sundae!"

CHAPTER 6
Anna May

We eat slowly. Grandma asks me questions about my family and my work. I should be astonished at how much she knows about me—nearly 45 years after our last conversation, the day before she died suddenly from a blood clot. I want to ask her about other family members who have died—especially my mother—but somehow it doesn't seem right, so I hold back.

"We weren't sure what to expect from you when you were a young man," she says once we've finished our dinner. "We knew that you were gifted in many ways, but you didn't seem to be interested in the things that the men in our family were all passionate about—sports, business and politics. We didn't quite know what to make of you."

I'm not sure I want our conversation to go this way. She has hit a sore spot for me and named one of the most painful and confusing issues I had to deal with growing up. Ironically, Grandma was one of the few adult family members who didn't make me feel like I was a failure simply because I was different.

But why was I different? I know that from a very young age I rebelled against my parents' expectations. I remember being scolded on my 6th birthday because I wanted to ride my new bike rather than play ball with my cousins (who were older and better at sports than I was). I also recall the many times I disappointed my father when he wanted me to play catch with him in the backyard but I was not interested.

"Don't be too hard on yourself, dear. You were just a child. We're the ones who should have known better."

"I know that's true, Grandma, but I was also at fault. I refused to play sports even when I knew how much it meant to Dad. I didn't have to be that self-centered."

51

"Pride goeth before destruction, and a haughty spirit before a fall," she says, quoting the Book of Proverbs. "Pride has certainly been our family's greatest struggle."

She clears the dining room table. (I am not allowed to help.) Then she brings out a gallon container of vanilla ice cream, a jar of Hershey's chocolate sauce, and an aerosol can of real whipped cream. Grandma doesn't cook. Ever. That's why Stouffer's heat-and-serve frozen foods are such a godsend. Once when my sister Anne and I spent the night, Grandma gave us chocolate sundaes for dinner and made us promise we wouldn't tell our mother.

Our conversation resumes once we've enjoyed our ice cream and all the dishes have been rinsed and neatly placed in the kitchen sink.

"Our family has been blessed in so many ways," she tells me now that we're seated in the sunroom. "My father's success gave me the opportunity to graduate from college and earn a master's degree in history at a time when most women my age were not well-educated. I learned to appreciate art and music and all the fine things in life. I'm afraid I took it all for granted, and, worse, came to expect it as somehow my right. Pride brings with it a sense of entitlement and a kind of blindness that can prevent us from seeing things as they truly are."

I remember Grandma playing Chopin on the baby grand piano in the living room of our home on Sydenham Road. It was not long after Grandpa Callaghan died in 1960, and she seemed to have lost her purpose in life. She was a small woman then, and very frail, with gray hair and sallow skin. My mother once told me that Grandma suffered several small strokes in the years before she died. She may have been diminished physically, but she was always alert and energetic and proud—especially when she was talking about the things that mattered most to her, usually her family and its many contributions to the Church and to society.

"How do we overcome our pride, Grandma? I'd really like to know. My whole life I have felt the weight of it holding me back and preventing me from really being free."

"I wish I could give you a simple answer, dear. Sometimes it's a rude awakening that causes us to see quite clearly (and painfully) that we are not in charge. Then we must let go. Occasionally we can achieve some degree of humility (the genuine kind, not the false façade) through prayer. I said many a rosary in my day, and I nearly wore out my prayer book asking God to help me. But I'm afraid that pain and disappointment are the most common ways that we learn to accept our own powerlessness. It's only when we can manage to surrender our pride willingly that we begin to experience lasting joy."

The sun is setting now, and we probably should turn on some lights, but there's something about sitting in the dark with my grandmother that is peaceful and comforting. I can feel the heaviness of sleep coming over me, and I begin to resist. I want to cry out: "Please God, don't take her away from me again!" but I feel myself slipping away uncontrollably. There's no use fighting it. No matter how much I want this dream to continue, I can't help waking up again.

"Don't worry, dear," I can hear Grandma's voice faintly; but I can't see her any more. "I'm here when you need me."

✳ ✳ ✳

A specialist with a very long name has been called in for a neurological consult. He tells Sharon there is hope. In some cases, swelling in the brain is what causes the coma. When the swelling subsides, many patients do recover. It's too early to know for sure, but the doctor with the long name is cautiously optimistic.

I still can't communicate with anyone to let them know I can hear them, and the frustration is unbearable. I'm not a patient person. I can't tell you how many times I've embarrassed my children by snapping at a store clerk or cursing at the driver in front of me. I once saw a bumper sticker on a pickup truck in Naples, Florida, that perfectly describes my chronic impatience. It said, "When I get old, I'm going to go up north and drive slow."

Lying in this hospital bed totally unable to communicate will either teach me patience or provoke insanity. When I'm awake, I try to be patient and to pray the *Memorare*. When I'm sleeping, I dream about the people I love who have died. I wonder if the doctor with the long name will be able to explain to me these maddening but wonderful dreams.

CHAPTER 7
Uncle Dan

We are sitting on the screened-in porch of the ranch-style house Uncle Dan built when he retired from the shipping business. His younger brother Tim, my grandfather, gave him a plot of land at the Conway Farm that overlooked a valley and pastureland below. Uncle Dan called it The Hideaway because it was nestled into the hillside and was a perfect escape from the hustle and bustle of the New York-New Jersey communities he lived and worked in all his adult life.

Uncle Dan never married. He was a sophisticate, a connoisseur of art and the theater, and a bit of a curmudgeon. When he retired at 60 (my age now), he spent six months traveling throughout Europe and Asia. Then he bought a modest home in Phoenix where he spent the winter, and he built The Hideaway as a summer residence to be near my Grandfather Conway and his large family.

Family members and friends would come to see him on weekends. To avoid having to serve complicated meals to unannounced guests, he always prepared a large pot of homemade vegetable soup, which simmered on the stove all day long. With a large slice of bread from Hough Bakery, Uncle Dan's vegetable soup was a hearty meal. Children were offered iced tea. Adults were served Carling's Black Label beer, or something harder.

Uncle Dan wears a polo shirt, neatly pressed slacks and sandals. He was "dapper" in his day, and he still looks tan and handsome at 70 something. He has a quick wit and a wry sense of humor, and he loves to make fun of relatives who rub him the wrong way. My cousins and I compete for the best Uncle Dan imitation, but Sally Conley wins every time. She has each gesture and inflection down perfectly. And she can mimic him for what seems like hours without cracking a smile—while the rest of us are splitting our sides with laughter!

"Danny, my boy. I'm glad you're here. Would you like some soup?"

"Yes, Uncle, and some iced tea."

"You're not drinking these days, I see. Probably a good idea. Too many drunks in our family."

I'm tempted to say that it's more complicated than that, but in fact he's hit the nail right on the head.

"Alcohol opens Pandora's box. It unleashes our most unruly desires, and all kinds of things are let out without our permission. As I always say, there are no skeletons in our family's closet. They all came out years ago!"

He hands me a large bowl of his vegetable soup. The aroma overwhelms me. The vegetables are all fresh from the garden. The seasonings are his own special blend. Several slices of bread, and some Land O'Lakes butter, are laid out on the kitchen counter next to a large pitcher of iced tea. ·

"Help yourself, my boy. Make yourself at home, but don't make a mess. I can't stand an untidy kitchen."

"Thanks, Uncle Dan. It's wonderful to be with you again. I've really missed you."

"I've watched you closely over the years," he says. "You've made many right choices since you became an adult. Giving up the booze helped you see things more clearly. You married a strong woman and together you have a good family. I was especially pleased when your last child, the only boy, was christened Daniel Richard. That was my father's name, you know; he was your great-grandfather."

"My father insisted we name him Daniel. I was thinking about calling him John, after Dad, but he wouldn't hear of it. He said that it's a Conway family tradition to name the first born son in every generation Daniel Richard. Dad was right. Family traditions are important."

"Not all of your choices have been good ones," he says looking right at me. "Even after you quit drinking, the unruly desires refused to be completely extinguished. And you never did figure out how to manage money successfully. You made a decent living, and you supported—and educated—your large family. But whatever happened to putting money aside for a rainy day? When the Social Security system collapses—it was a terrible idea to begin with—you'll be living on the streets!"

"You're right, Uncle. I've not always been a good steward. I've not always practiced what I preach. I'm afraid that makes me a hypocrite."

"It makes you a human being. Stop thinking you're supposed to be perfect. At your age, I discovered that daily Mass and frequent confession were necessary to keep me on the straight and narrow. It wouldn't hurt you to be a little more regular and consistent in your practice of the faith."

"Yes, Uncle. You're right." If I ever get out of this hospital bed, I'll be a lot more faithful."

"Our family has been exposed to every conceivable temptation," Uncle Dan says. "We know the sins of the flesh as well as the sins of avarice, envy, gluttony, anger and indifference. You can't help being human, but you sure as hell don't have to give up trying to be better. Prayer is not for weaklings. It's for people who want to be mature, honest and healthy human beings."

When I was young, it never occurred to me that Uncle Dan was someone who struggled with "unruly desires" or that he prayed the rosary or attended daily Mass as part of a conscious decision to be a better man. He's right about me. I need to practice my faith in a more robust way. I need to grow spiritually and become a better man.

"Your Great Aunt Connie called just before you got here. She wants you to know that she sees your mother often and that she is well. Connie also told me to tell you that your grandparents are also well. We're all working to overcome the sins of our past lives and, with God's help, to be ready when the Lord calls us to Himself. Please pray for us. We need it."

"Then you are not yet in heaven?" I had assumed that by now they would all be with God.

"We are no longer 'on the way' as you are, but there is a process we must go through to become ready for heaven. This is the true object of all our desiring, the genuine hope that we aspire to with our whole heart and soul. Your prayers can make a difference in our possession of true joy— just as our prayers for you can help keep you on the path to holiness."

"I will pray for you, Uncle Dan, and for all the family who have died. Please pray for me as well. I need to get out of this hospital so I can go home and set things straight!"

＊ ＊ ＊

My daughter Margaret, who is a nurse, and my niece Carolyn, who is a doctor, are in the room with me. Things can't be too bad. They are laughing.

I wish I could get their attention, but it's no use. They're focused on something else, a trip we took several weeks ago to see their cousin Mick's final performance at L'École Nationale de Cirque in Montreal. Mick is now a certified circus performer, a clown, acrobat and juggler. His final performance had us all in stitches. Carolyn and Margaret are obviously reliving those precious moments!

If only I could get them to look at me, but what good would it do? I can't talk to them or ask them any questions. I can only hope ... and dream.

CHAPTER 8
Mr. Rini

I am on a terrace in the Ristorante Rosiello in Possillipo, Italy, over-looking the Bay of Naples. It is one of the most beautiful places in the world—very like the Isle of Capri but without the upscale tourists and outrageous prices. With me is Mr. Rini who was a second father to me during my high school and college years. His son Tom was one of my best friends growing up, and I spent many happy days at the Rini home on Fairmount Boulevard.

Mr. Rini was a hardworking man. He woke up at 4 a.m. six days a week in order to be at the Northern Ohio Food Terminal early in the morning when his wholesale fruit and vegetable company, Thomas M. Rini and Sons, opened for business. When I knew him, Mr. Rini suffered from migraine headaches and chronic sleep deprivation. I remember one day, when he was sitting at the kitchen table trying to read the newspa-per, he threw off his glasses and exclaimed with great frustration, "I can't see with these damn things, and I can't see without them!" He was a kind and generous man, but he often felt that because of his work he was missing the best things in his life, especially his wife, Jo, and his two daughters and three sons.

"How long have you been coming to Italy?" he asks me in between the first course, *scialatielli* (a form of pasta unique to this region), and the main dish, *scallopine capriciosa* (veal with peas, ham and mushrooms).

"My first trip was 13 years ago in 1996. I was on a pilgrimage led by Archbishop Daniel Buechlein of Indianapolis, and my parents were with me. It was their first and only trip to Italy, but I've been back near-ly every year since then—sometimes twice a year."

"And why Naples? Most Americans prefer the quiet beauty and romance of Tuscany."

"I've been to Tuscany (Siena), Umbria (Assisi), the Marches (Pesaro) and several of the cities in Northern Italy. And my business frequently takes me to Rome and the Vatican. But Naples is my first choice in all of Italy. I'm not sure why."

"Naples gets under your skin," he says.

It's an old slogan from a 19th century travel brochure, but it's certainly true in my case. A similar old saying, "See Naples and die," is not something I want to think about in my present condition.

The view from this terrace overlooks the rooftops of the houses beneath us as well as the lush trees and gardens that scale down the cliff between us and the sea below. The water is a distinctive shade of blue (*azzurro* the Italians call it). From this vantage point the low-hanging clouds appear to be eye level, only much further out over the bay, which suggests that if our arms were only long enough we could reach out and touch them.

"Italy is full of illusions," Mr. Rini says. "Don't get too caught up in all this or you'll end up disappointed."

"I know that's true, but I can't help myself. When I'm here the problems of everyday life seem really far away. Please don't tell my Irish ancestors, but I think I was born with an Italian soul."

"In spite of all their differences, the Irish and the Italians share the same fundamental values—faith, family and a special love for our own people," Mr. Rini says. "I married an Irish girl, so our children got the best of both worlds."

"Well, the Italians sure express things differently. We Irish tend to be introverts who keep our emotions inside us. Italians are the reverse. Everything is 'up front and in your face.' I suspect I keep coming back to Italy for the same reason I love Italian opera. It allows me to experience vicariously passions that I would otherwise repress."

"You work too hard, like I did," Mr. Rini says. "That's a problem you should face squarely and try to change. Escaping to Italy once or twice a year is wonderful, if you can do it, but you really need to learn to relax in your own home with your family. I did it late in my life with great difficulty, but if it was possible for me, you can do it too."

I remember Mr. Rini sitting in his living room listening to Big Band music from the 1940s surrounded by hundreds of records and tapes. He worked hard at learning to relax (or so it seemed to me).

"You're right, Mr. Rini. Thank you. And thanks for all the times you welcomed me into your home and treated me like your son. Please give my love to Mrs. Rini. I'm sorry I missed her funeral, but I'm really pleased that the two of you are together again."

"By the way, Dan, I was just talking to Bill Dempsey and Charlie Bacon and several more of your friends' parents. They told me lots of stories about the days when you kids got together during summers at Madison on the Lake. I know how much those days meant to my Tommy and to young Charlie and Dawn and all your friends."

"Those were great times," I say. "As close to 'carefree days' as I can remember. That's what Italy is like for me now: time out of time, a world apart from anxious cares. But you're right to warn me, Mr. Rini. I know these experiences can't last. They are just glimpses of a better world to come."

The restaurant is now filled with Italian families who have come for *pranzo*, their Sunday dinner. Mr. Rini pays the bill, refusing to let me contribute, and we begin the long walk down the Via Possillipo toward Naples. This is one dream I wouldn't mind stretching out for many more days. But, to tell the truth, I miss Sharon and our family and I really do need to get well again so that I can go home and get back to work as soon as possible.

CHAPTER 9
Rita

She is sitting in her comfortable chair in her large family home on Tanager Trail in Brecksville on Cleveland's south side. She is smoking a cigarette and drinking a beer. I am her favorite son-in-law (her only son-in-law) and with me she always "tells it like it is."

"You are a member of this family," she says. "Don't you forget that." By family, she means her 10 children (2 daughters and 8 sons), their spouses and her 26 grandchildren. "Nothing is more important than family. Don't forget that."

She is a passionate woman, very beautiful and self-possessed. When I first met her she was in her late 50s. I remember being struck by the way she carried herself. She lived to be almost 90 but she retained a youthful appearance that was not superficial (an old woman trying to appear young) but a true example of what is meant by the expression "young at heart." She grew older, and suffered many infirmities, but she never lost her curiosity, her humor or her love of life, so her youth and beauty shone through in spite of her age.

Although she experienced a long and painful death that stripped her of everything physical and material, I see her now as she was when I first met her, when I first fell in love with her daughter Sharon. She is lovely and full of life. She is strong-willed and determined to protect her family. Above all, she wants to keep them (us) together. She wants us to "be there" for one another and for her.

I am never quite sure what to call her. Mrs. Hudec would be too formal, but Rita seems too familiar. Mother is OK but not quite right. I have my own mother. Most of the time I call her Grandma, which is what my children call her.

"What's it like to be in heaven, Grandma? Have you been reunited with your parents and your sisters and brothers?"

"I was never really separated from them," she says. "Family bonds are stronger than death because they are forged with love. Even people who are estranged during their lifetime never really lose their connection to family."

"What about Sharon's father," I ask. "Have you been reconciled with him?"

"The things that separated us in life don't matter here," she says. "I remember my mother telling me that no house is big enough for two families. (Al and I lived with my parents for a short time after we were married.) But God's house has many mansions—many dimensions—and there's room for everyone here."

"What was it like—the long passage from life through death to the place where you are now? Was it frightening and painful?"

"Yes. I was terrified and the pain was awful. But the love of my family sustained me. Their presence, their prayers, their overwhelming support and comfort carried me through the hard times. God's grace was working overtime in them. That made the unbearable bearable. It gave me courage and hope. It told me—without any doubt or hesitation—that I was not alone. I've always believed that nothing is more important than my family, but my death convinced me of this absolutely. If you have faith, and a loving family, you can get through anything."

"Is there anything I can do for you, Grandma?" As I ask the question, it seems strange to me. What could I—lying in bed in a coma—possibly do for her?

"Pray for me," she says. "It's important. It keeps us connected—to each other and to God."

"I promise, Rita. I will pray for you always, like I pray for my Mom and for all the members of my family who have died. It does keep us together as family."

"Don't ever forget that," she says.

★ ★ ★

As my eyes open, I see Sharon sitting beside my bed. She looks like Rita did when I first met her. She is strong and lovely and equally determined to protect her family. These days there are lots of things out there in the world pulling families apart. I thank God for Sharon and for the incredibly strong women I have known and loved who have given their lives to keep their (our) families together. I think especially of my grandmothers—Anna May and Margaret—my aunts Mary and Joan, and of course my mother, Helen, and my mother-in-law, Rita.

How could I forget that I am a member of their family or act as if family didn't matter to me? None of them would let me have any peace at all if I were so foolish, and so ungrateful, that I forgot who I am or to whom I belong.

Nothing is more important than family because family binds us to each other and to God, who is Father, Son and Spirit in one communion of eternal, life-giving love.

I promise not to forget this—but to do my very best to stay connected with my family always through my presence, my prayer and the power of life-giving love.

CHAPTER 10
Thursday

I wake up in a strange place, a public house or bar room that I've never been in before. Behind the bar is a large, portly man with disheveled hair and glasses—the old-fashioned kind that sit on the bridge of his nose with a ribbon attached to his vest.

The man is hauntingly familiar, but for the life of me I don't know who he is. My Grandfather Conway had a friend named Charlie Otis who looked a little bit like this man. (I remember seeing him in family pictures, but I don't think I ever met him.) Could this be Mr. Otis?

I'm uneasy. Until now, the people I've met in these dreams have all been family members or close friends, people I grew up with who meant a lot to me. This man is different. I wouldn't say he is a stranger because of the uncanny sense of familiarity I feel in his presence. But one thing is certain. This encounter will be different.

The man is puttering behind the bar. He's not the bartender, but he is definitely comfortable pouring drinks. He appears to be humming a familiar tune. I think it's a Gilbert and Sullivan patter song, but I can't quite tell. Suddenly he breaks into song, *"As someday it may happen that a victim must be found ...."* It's the executioner's song from *The Mikado.* *"I've got a little list. I've got a little list. Of society's offenders who might well be underground and who never will be missed. Who never will be missed."*

"Excuse me, sir," I say hesitantly, not wanting to be added to his list. "Have we met before?"

"Thursday," he replies, rather absent-mindedly.

"I beg your pardon, sir, but Thursday was the day before my accident, and I don't recall meeting you then or at any other time in my adult life. Are you my grandfather's friend, Mr. Otis?"

"Never met the fellow," the strange gentleman replies. "Is he a man of wit? Wit is a more manly exercise than fiddling or fooling. Wit

75

requires an intellectual athleticism because it is akin to logic. Mark Twain was a man of wit. He did not want excitement. He occasioned it."

"I'm very confused, sir, and a little frightened. You see, I was in an accident last week, and I'm in a coma, and I've been having these dreams. Until now, everyone in my dreams has been someone I knew intimately before they died. But you, sir, are unknown to me."

"Come now, it's not as bad as all that. Have a drink with me."

"I'm afraid I can't do that, sir. I don't drink."

"Teetotaler?"

"Well, not exactly," I reply. "I don't object to other people drinking—as long as they can handle it."

"You're quite right, my good man," he says emptying his glass and pouring another. "A man who drinks normally makes an ordinary man of himself. But a man who drinks excessively makes a complete fool of himself. My doctor says I shouldn't drink alcohol, but a little milk punch never hurt anyone."

Milk punch? My Grandfather Callaghan used to drink milk punch "for medicinal purposes." He'd mix 2 ounces of Kentucky Bourbon with 3 ounces of Dairymen's homogenized milk and then add a teaspoon of sugar. If I weren't already in a coma, I could quickly achieve the same result by drinking several glasses of milk punch.

Before I can respond, he continues. "Once, on a train from Boston to New York, I was forced to listen to the incoherent ramblings of a vegetarian who was also a teetotaler. Try as I might, I could see absolutely no connection between consuming vegetables and not consuming fermented vegetables. A drunkard, I observed, when lifted laboriously out of the gutter, might well be heard huskily to plead that he had fallen there through excessive devotion to a vegetable diet."

"What did you say your name was, sir?" I am desperate to change the subject and make some sense out of all this.

"You may call me Thursday. It's not my real name, of course, but I've adopted it in the interests of national security."

"OK, uh. Mr. Thursday. Where are you from?"

"I currently reside in a place that is a lot like Cleveland. Even if you love it and belong to it, you still can't make head or tail of it."

"Sounds a lot like this dream," I say. I'm hoping I'll wake up soon.

"The reason you're having this particular dream," the man who calls himself Thursday says to me in a rare moment of clarity, "is to prevent you from taking yourself too seriously. Humility is the mother of giants," he says. "And humor is the only cure for madness."

This dream is beginning to remind me of a comic opera by Rossini. "Enough! Please!" I scream silently to myself. I don't want to offend Mr. Thursday, who might still be my grandfather's friend gone batty, but I've had enough of this.

I'm awake again, and I feel like crying—not because I'm sad, but because I can't handle all the emotions these dreams provoke in me. The English writer G. K. Chesterton once said, "Dreams, like life, are full of nobility and joy, but of a nobility and joy utterly arbitrary and incalculable. We have gratitude, but never certainty."

My mother used to say the same thing. We have gratitude, not certainty, and humor, the only cure for madness.

CHAPTER 11
Aunt Joan

I'm in a Jewish delicatessen in Cleveland. I think it's Corky and Lenny's. I'm sitting in a booth with Aunt Joan, my mother's sister. She orders a Reuben sandwich. I have chicken salad on rye.

During the final years of her life, Aunt Joan was legally blind. As a result, she didn't get out of the house much. Whenever I was in town (she lived in Chesterland on the far east side of Cleveland), I would take her out to lunch.

Those lunches were the least I could do to repay Aunt Joan for the many times that she rescued me from painful childhood experiences. I grew up in an alcoholic home, and there were days when the pain and embarrassment were unbearable. Vacations were always the worst times. I'm not sure what I expected. Fun probably. Vacations should be fun. But I came to hate vacations, dread them really, because they were not fun at all. They were painful, embarrassing, hurtful times. Vacations didn't help me escape from my loneliness, anger or fear. They only made me feel worse.

My worst vacation was a trip to Oglebay Park in West Virginia when I was 12 or 13. It was a spectacularly beautiful place. The mountains were imposing and mysterious. The forests were larger and more densely wooded than the ones I used to explore at my grandparents' homes in northeast Ohio. The park offered everything a vacationing family could hope for—an Olympic size swimming pool, playgrounds, golf, horseback riding, hiking and lots more. It should have been great fun, but it wasn't. It was horrible. Humiliating. A time of deep sadness.

Vacations are no fun when your parents are fighting. I remember lying in bed probably around midnight the first night we arrived at the park. We were in a cabin and the walls were paper thin. My parents were arguing and I heard a loud crash. My father had smashed a bottle of Old Grand-Dad on a coffee table and the shattering glass cut my mother's

81

arm. I remember him screaming, "I'm not ever going on vacation with a bottle of booze again." I could hear my mother crying, and I cried too. And then I fell asleep—knowing somehow that tomorrow would be even worse.

On many of those occasions, Aunt Joan somehow knew that I was at a breaking point. "Hey, Dan, why don't you come and stay with us for a while?" she would say. She never had to ask me twice.

"Do you remember the time I served you kids wieners and sauerkraut for dinner?" she asks, savoring her Reuben.

"I sure do. You told us that we had to eat all our sauerkraut, and I couldn't do it. I really tried, but the vinegar and spices were too much for me."

"I hope I wasn't too hard on you," she says with a knowing smile.

"Are you kidding? I was the only one who didn't have to bring you a clean plate. My cousins never let me forget it!"

Aunt Joan led a hard life with lots of emotional and financial problems. Even as a child I knew that her kindness to me was above and beyond the call of duty. She had plenty of other things to worry about—including her own needs and those of her children.

After her youngest son, Charley, died in a motorcycle accident when he was in his twenties, Aunt Joan gave my mother a poem she wrote.

> *God lent him to me for a while*
> *To get to know his friendly smile*
> *To know how very much life meant*
> *That every precious moment spent*
> *Might be his last and that is why*
> *He was prepared to live or die.*
>
> *He was a funny kind of kid*
> *In what he said and what he did.*
> *He had a whole lot of friends*
> *And as if to make amends*
> *To free us all of any guilt*
> *He lived his life right to the hilt.*

He did a lot of things for me
That other people didn't see.
He'd call me on the phone and say
I love you, Mom, and in that way
He let me know when he was gone
He wanted me to carry on.

Aunt Joan carried on. She was a survivor. And my mother, who was an award-winning poet and a professor of English literature, saved this poem, and treasured it, not because it's great poetry but because she knew what it meant to Aunt Joan to be able to express her grief in this way and to share it with someone who would understand.

My lunch conversations with Aunt Joan usually looked backward to happier days in her life, but today she is focused on the future.

"When your time comes, Dan, you'll discover that all the things we hope for in life, if they're genuine, can only be realized after our death. The choice is ours. We can either cling to the past or let go of it. And the wonderful thing is that when we let go, we discover that we haven't lost anything after all. Our memories and all our precious possessions become visibly part of who we are, now and always, in the joy of heaven."

"Can you tell me what heaven is like?" I ask knowing that I probably won't get a simple answer.

"Joy is the only word that even comes close to describing it," she speaks softly, almost reverently. "Heaven is where our deepest desires, our greatest longings, are fulfilled. The aching emptiness and bitter disappointments that we knew on earth are gone. Forever."

We're finished with our sandwiches, and the young man who is our waiter asks if we've saved room for desert.

"You're darn right we have," Aunt Joan tells him. "I'll have the Boston cream pie. I spied it coming in here in the glass case at the front of the restaurant. It looks delicious!"

"I'll just have decaf coffee," I say, "I'm watching my weight." Aunt Joan scolds me. "This is only a dream, you know. There are no calories in dreams. And you're already asleep for goodness sake," she says. Have some real coffee and a piece of pie."

I order the coconut cream pie and a cup of regular coffee.

"It's hard to visualize everlasting life," I say. "It sounds really boring. What do you do all day long?"

"You can't visualize it. For one thing, time doesn't exist in heaven, so you can't think of it in earthly categories like 'all day long.' And in heaven no one is full of himself, which is what boredom means—being too stuffed with yourself to be interested in anyone or anything else. Hell is boring. Heaven is just the opposite."

"Are you in heaven now, Aunt Joan? Everyone else I've talked to in these dreams seems to be in some intermediate state. You talk as if your deepest desires have already been fulfilled."

"This is something else you can't quite grasp, Dan. The 'time' between our earthly death and the lasting joy of heaven (or the excruciating sadness of hell) isn't time at all. And it isn't a place. We are with God. Beyond that, I don't know what to say."

"But the others have led me to believe that you are not asleep. You're aware of what's going on in the land of the living, and in some real way you are engaged or involved with us. Is that true?"

"Definitely. It's just that now our means of engagement is spiritual not material."

"What does that mean exactly, Aunt Joan? Spirituality is such an abstract concept. Surely you don't mean that you're involved in our world the way spirits are in ghost stories. Everything I've learned in these dreams tells me that you are much more than disembodied spirits who inhabit the dark and depressing places of the world."

"That's right, Dan. We are not ghosts, and we're not angels. We are human beings who are being transformed—from a state of spiritual incompleteness and physical corruption to new life in Christ. We're not in heaven yet. We still have choices to make, and sins to atone for. The difference is that we now see with much greater clarity the joy that lies ahead. As a result, our hope is much more vibrant and our desires are much more easily satisfied."

Lunch with Aunt Joan was always a treat, but today is really special. Her sadness and disappointment, which were always just beneath the surface, are nowhere to be found today. She is happy and at peace. As she said, her hope is much more vibrant.

"I love you, Aunt Joan."

"I know, Dan. You always have."

"Be at peace now," she tells me. You have plenty of time left to share your life with Sharon and your children. And when you see my children, tell them that I love you all and I'm waiting for the day when all of us will be together again."

Do I really have lots of time left, or is Aunt Joan just trying to make me feel better the way she did when I was young?

I sure hope she's right.

CHAPTER 12
Archbishop Murphy

This is not Cleveland. The skyscrapers are taller and more numerous. The streets are more crowded with tourists and shoppers. The lakefront is more developed—with condos and boat docks and a pier that looks like a long and narrow shopping mall.

This is not Cleveland. It's Chicago. I'm on the corner of Rush and Superior right in front of the Rosebud restaurant that has the best fried calamari in the world. Why am I here?

I have an ambivalent relationship with the city of Chicago. I worked here for two years in the late 1990s, and I respect this city's many accomplishments and its vitality. (Cleveland is a ghost town by comparison.) But I bristle at the hubris of Chicagoans. To their way of thinking, no city is as good as Chicago, and no one who was not born and raised here can ever quite measure up to their standards.

"You really need to get over your hang-ups about my hometown." The voice is familiar and the smile and white hair are unmistakable. "You know how much this city, and this archdiocese, means to me, Dan. Although I'll never understand what took them so long to make stewardship a priority here."

Thomas J. Murphy died more than 12 years ago in Seattle where he served as archbishop following a brief stint as the bishop of Great Falls-Billings, Montana, and many years as a priest, faculty member and then rector of St. Mary of the Lake Seminary (Mundelein) here in the Archdiocese of Chicago. When he died, he was only 5 years older than I am now. His final years of ministry were devoted to teaching stewardship as a way of living the Gospel.

Of all the dedicated and faith-filled people who taught me my profession, Archbishop Murphy had the greatest personal impact on my life. His death really threw me. It forced me to accept that I have been called to follow in his footsteps as a witness to the powerful, but largely unexplored, concept of Christian stewardship. I was writing about, and teaching, stewardship before Archbishop Murphy died. In fact, we often taught together, which was a great joy. But after his death, what had previously been just one dimension of my professional career became its primary focus. It was as if he bequeathed to me his passion and his single-minded dedication to teaching stewardship as a way of life.

"Do you remember how I used to say that letting go, admitting we're not in control, is the hardest form of poverty?"

"I sure do, Archbishop," I say, still feeling embarrassed that he has exposed my prejudice about Chicago.

"Letting go is important in big things and in little things," he says.

(My guess is that, for him, negative feelings about his hometown falls in the category of big things.)

"I know, Archbishop. Somehow letting go gets harder as I get older, but I'm working on it."

You'd think that by now I'd have long since outgrown this kind of parochialism. I've lived in Kentucky for more than 25 years now, and I really do love it, but when you get right down to it, Cleveland is still my home—just as Chicago is Archbishop Murphy's.

"Not being in control isn't difficult to grasp intellectually," the archbishop says, "but it's very hard emotionally. I struggled with it my whole life. The concept of stewardship helped me understand this otherwise negative truth in a positive light. If we recognize everything as a gift that we have received from a good and gracious God, then letting go can be seen not as losing something that belongs to us but as giving it back to its rightful owner out of gratitude.

"Growing up in Chicago helped me appreciate the importance of family, faith and community. These are critical elements in the formation of each human being. If any one of these is missing or weak, the person suffers in his or her maturity."

We've been walking up Rush Street, and we're now at the Archbishop Quigley Center, the former minor seminary building that now houses the chancery and other archdiocesan offices.

"I was blessed with a strong family, a vibrant faith and a wonderful community life," the archbishop says. The only appropriate response to these amazing gifts is gratitude."

"My mother used to talk about gratitude," I say. "When I was 18, I decided I'd had enough, and I announced I was leaving home and not coming back.

My mother said, "Just be sure to say thank you as you walk out the door."

"But it wasn't easy to be grateful. Our family life wasn't always happy. My mother was drinking heavily then, and my father was distracted by problems at work and at home. My sisters and brothers and I basically took care of ourselves, but it was a tough time for all of us. Our chaotic family life colored my attitude toward the Church and what I perceived to be its harsh rules and archaic rituals. Even in our parish elementary school, many of my classmates and I rebelled against the Catholic worldview that was presented to us by the priests and nuns who taught us religion. By the time I was in high school, I didn't want any part of it. I had given up on the Church and I had serious doubts about family life and about our society. (It was the 1960s, and my generation held nothing sacred—except our longing for self-expression and freedom from restraint!)"

"What changed?" the archbishop asks. "This is obviously not the way you feel now."

"The summer after I graduated from high school I had this overwhelming desire to do something with my life that would help people, that would make a difference in the world. I was scheduled to go to college in the fall and my plan was to major in communications (television broadcasting), but suddenly that didn't seem good enough. I wanted something more. And although I had rejected the Church as outdated and irrelevant, I couldn't think of anything more important or worth while than being a Catholic priest totally dedicated to serving God and helping people."

"I know you ended up with the Benedictines in southern Indiana," the archbishop says. "How did you get there?"

"I had an uncle who was a priest, and when I told him that I was thinking about the priesthood, he suggested that I go to Saint Meinrad and try it out. That decision changed my life forever, and the eight years I spent there transformed me from a very confused and unhappy young man to a reasonably mature and faith-filled adult. The chaos and emotional immaturity of my early years were given form and direction by the stability and the ordered spirituality of the Benedictine way of life, which greatly influenced me during those very important years. Eventually I discovered that I was not called to be a monk or priest. My vocation is marriage, and my goal in life is to be a mature Catholic layman wholly dedicated to my family, my Church and my community."

The archbishop is nodding compassionately. *"What do I own and what owns me?"* he says. "Do you remember the first time I asked you this stewardship question?"

"Yes, Archbishop. It was nearly 20 years ago in Seattle during our first extended conversation about stewardship. You were very gracious to me that day, and your passion for stewardship was contagious!"

"You could say that you were once owned by chaos and confusion, and that now you are owned by the generous and loving God who has given you everything—faith, family and the great work that you are called to do with and for the Church. You've been given many precious gifts, my friend. Remember that one day you will be asked to render an account."

This subject—accountability—makes me uncomfortable in the best of circumstances, but in my present condition, lying in bed in a coma subject to all these uncanny dreams, the last thing I want to think about is the Final Judgment. I've got a whole lot more work to do before I'm at all ready to answer for my stewardship of God's gifts!

Archbishop Murphy and I have stopped walking, and we're in front of the old seminary building. We stop in the chapel at the Quigley Center to visit the Blessed Sacrament. Whenever I enter a church, I say this prayer of St. Francis: *We praise you, Lord, and we bless you, in this church and in all the churches of the world because by your Holy Cross you have redeemed the world.* Somehow it helps me to feel connected and at home wherever I happen to be.

The archbishop is kneeling, totally engrossed in prayer. I am distracted. I know this is a dream, so I'm tempted to maintain a safe emotional distance from all this.

As I watch the archbishop, I notice for the first time that he looks different somehow. In the years that I knew him, he always seemed emaciated and slightly disheveled. Now his skin is clear and his eyes have nothing of the strained and bloodshot look that was always so evident, especially when he was tired. (The truth is that he didn't take very good care of himself.) But now, if you tried to guess his age, you'd almost certainly get it wrong. He looks like a mature adult, a cleric in a black suit and Roman collar, but he appears ageless and perfectly healthy.

When he's finished praying, he turns to me and says, "We all have to render an account of our stewardship. But most of us miss the point. We think we'll be judged on our accomplishments or our failures. That's not what God cares about. He doesn't care one darn bit who we are, what we own, what we've done or what we've failed to do."

"I'm not quite following you, Archbishop. What else would we be accountable for if not our successes and failures at living a good Christian life? Didn't you teach us that one day God would ask each one of us, 'What did you do with all the gifts and talents I gave you? Did you nurture and grow them; did you share them with others; or did you squander them through abuse or neglect'"

"Yes, that's what I taught you," the archbishop says with a passionate intensity that reminds me of his stewardship talks, "and I was partially right, but I missed the main point."

"And what would that be, Archbishop?"

"You remember the parable in Matthew's Gospel when the King (Christ) tells us that on the Last Day we'll be judged according to whether we fed the hungry, clothed the naked, visited prisoners and so on? The way the Lord expresses this he makes it very personal. As long as we did it, or didn't do it, for the least of our brothers and sisters, we did it—or didn't do it—for him."

"Those Gospel sayings always make me uneasy," I say. "The Gospel sets a very high standard for us."

"What we fail to recognize" the archbishop says, "is the profoundly personal dimension of Christ's words. Feeding the hungry is a good thing in and of itself, but as Mother Teresa of Calcutta always insisted, it has to be an activity we do 'to Jesus, with Jesus and for Jesus.' The meaning of our lives—the basis on which we'll be judged—is not determined by our successes or failures or even how well we live the moral and spiritual values we believe in. What we will be judged on is how much we love God. Of course, the measure of our love is found in what we do, or don't do, and that includes feeding the hungry, clothing the naked, caring for the sick—what we used to call the corporal works of mercy. But the most important question is *did we love Jesus or did we love ourselves?* Did we recognize him in everything and everyone or were we blinded by our own selfishness and sin?"

"I think you're being too hard on yourself, Archbishop. The stewardship question that you gave us expresses your point perfectly. *What do I own and what owns me?* Am I owned wholly and completely by a good and gracious God? Or am I owned by my addictions and compulsions—to sex, to alcohol, to fame or prestige or to material things?"

"Yes, Dan, it's important to examine our conscience on a daily basis and to ask ourselves the stewardship question. But in the end the only question that really matters is: *What is my relationship to Jesus Christ? Do I know him intimately? Do I serve him in everything I say and do? Do I love him with all my heart, mind and soul?* If the answer to these questions is yes, then we will be happy with him in heaven.

"Take, Lord, and receive all my liberty; my memory, my understanding, and my entire will." The archbishop is saying the prayer of St. Ignatius Loyola.

★ ★ ★

When I think about Archbishop Murphy, I'm reminded of the apostles—ordinary men chosen by Jesus to do extraordinary things. Pope Benedict says that the apostles were given a paradoxical double assignment: to remain with Jesus and to go out into the world to carry his message to others.

A Christian steward also has a double assignment: to hold onto, and care for, all God's gifts, and then to let go of them, sharing them generously with others *out of love for Jesus.*

Archbishop Murphy has done it again. He's spoken to my heart, and he's challenged me to conversion. Clearly I have work to do. To know Jesus, love Jesus and serve Jesus—not half-heartedly with reservations and conditions, but fully and completely…

CHAPTER 13
Margaret

I'm in a train station. I think it's Cleveland's Terminal Tower, but it's been so long since I've been down here that I'm not quite sure. The station is nearly empty and it's eerily quiet. No announcements are being made, and there's no background music. The few people who are here either walk noiselessly to their destinations or sit quietly, or sleep, on benches in the waiting area.

Am I going somewhere? Or am I waiting for someone? I don't have any luggage or a train ticket, so I suppose I'm going to meet someone here. I sit down and wait.

All my other dreams have taken place in the present—in the year of my car accident—in spite of the fact that most of the people who visit me in these dreams are long dead. But this dream feels different. The few people I have seen here are dressed up, the way travelers used to dress in the 1940s. All my other dreams have been in color—often vividly so. This dream is more like an old movie or photograph with light and shadows that appear striking and expressive in spite of the fact the images are in various shades of black and white.

A woman is walking toward me. She's wearing an unmistakable old-fashioned hat and a long dress with sensible shoes. She's a large woman in her mid 50s with kind eyes and a gentle smile. She's carrying a small suitcase and an oversized purse that is full to overflowing.

She stops in the middle of the terminal and sits down on one of the benches across from me. Is she expecting someone to meet her? After a few quiet moments, she begins to sing softly:

When the moon comes over the mountain
Every beam brings a dream, dear, of
Once again we'll stroll 'neath the mountain
Through that rose-covered valley we knew.*

99

I'm sure that I have never met this woman before, but at the same time she seems very familiar. She reminds me of my father's sisters, and of many of my cousins, especially Aunt Mary's daughters. As I watch her more closely, her smile, and her physical and vocal resemblance to Kate Smith, gives her away. This can only be my Grandmother Conway who died in 1948, the year before I was born.

They said that Margaret Nelson Conway was a casualty of the Second World War. Her first-born son, for whom I was named, was killed in an Army Air Corps flight-training accident. Four more of her 11 sons, including my father, served in various branches of the Armed Services during the war. My Uncle Bill Conway, a middle child, was too young to serve. He remembers coming home from Gesu School one day and finding his mother kneeling on the floor with her back to him folding socks. When he went up to greet her, he discovered that she was crying. The fear and anxiety she lived with during those years took its toll. She died at age 53, leaving five young children, my father's four youngest brothers and his little sister, to be raised by my Grandfather Conway with the help of a succession of nannies who were capable and well-intentioned but who simply could not substitute for a mother's love.

"Excuse me. Are you Margaret Conway? I'm Jack's son, Dan."

"Oh, of course, Danny. I should have recognized you right away. You have your mother's hair and eyes."

"May I call you Grandmother?"

"Certainly. Please forgive me. I've been so distracted. I'm so proud of you—and all my grandchildren. I'm just sorry I didn't have the chance to share in your childhood. Of course, I watched you all closely and I prayed for you, all of you, every day."

"Do you really watch over us, Grandmother, and do you really know us, in spite of the fact that you died before we were born?"

"Oh, yes. The connections between the living and the dead are much stronger than you realize. Besides we're family and that bond remains strong even after death."

"I sometimes think that family is a mixed blessing," I say hesitatingly. "Growing up in the Conway family was hard sometimes—for me and

I believe for my sisters and brothers and all of our cousins. We had lots of reasons to celebrate—successes in business and sports and a rich family history. But there were also painful experiences to deal with and overcome—many of them resulting from the effects of alcoholism."

"I know, Dan. There were "family problems" from the beginning of my courtship and marriage to your grandfather. My family wasn't sure I'd be happy married to a penniless young Irishman—as he was at the time. They even predicted, accurately as it turned out, that I would end up with 13 children! On the other hand, your Great-Grandmother Conway was appalled that her Timmy would marry a Nelson. (Even though our ancestry was uncertain, probably Swedish, she assumed we were English.) But your grandfather and I made it work. We loved each other deeply, and we sacrificed (especially in the early years) to establish a loving home for our rapidly growing family.

"I used to be embarrassed when people would describe us as 'the perfect family,'" she says. "We were never perfect. We were a large loving family with many blessings but also with lots of challenges and imperfections. Your grandfather and I did the best we could, but it wasn't easy. When our son Dan died in 1941, and the war and military service threatened to take four more of the boys, including your father, I could hardly bear it. But I was never one to complain. We had too many blessings to be thankful for—and too much work to do raising our large family!"

"You know, Grandmother, it wasn't all bad. In fact, we had lots of good times when I was growing up—especially on weekends, and during the summer, when we went out to the farm. If our cousins were there, it was extra special. We rode horses together and went exploring in the woods beyond the pasture. We sneaked cigarettes when the adults weren't looking and smoked them in several different hiding places. (My favorite was the roof of the garage.)

During summer evenings at the farm, Tommy Conley and I would put on skits, comic sketches with music borrowed from many different sources including folk music and rock 'n' roll tunes from the '60s. Our aunts and uncles were a great audience. They laughed loudly and encouraged us to do more. Because we got together so often at the farm, we were close. We laughed a lot and teased each other the way close friends do. Although many years have separated us, and we now tend to see each other only at funerals and the occasional family reunion, there is a common bond among us.

Those were great days. We were innocent and fun-loving—in spite of the many problems we were facing as children in troubled families. We were happy together back then. Nothing and no one can take that away from us. It makes me feel good to think of those days, Grandmother. They didn't last long, but their mark on us was indelible. As my mother used to say, pain recedes and loses its power but happiness is forever."

"Your dear mother was right. Even now in this intermediate state we're in after death, joy and pain coexist for us —at least until the Last Day. And for us, time is not as you experience it. Once the world comes to its end and everything has been decided by our just and merciful God, things will assume their rightful places. Then, as the Bible says, "every tear will be wiped away." But until then, we share each other's suffering. Mind you, we have no doubt that love is stronger than death or that joy is waiting for us if only we choose to embrace it and hold onto it with all our strength. That's why we pray that everyone, even the most hopeless sinner, will one day seek God's forgiveness and be saved."

"The 'intermediate state' you're in—is that purgatory?"

"Thank heaven, no. I had my purgatory on earth. I'm with Christ now, waiting for the end-time, and I'm fundamentally at peace. But I can't rest completely until all my children and grandchildren have made their final choices. I love you all and pray for each of you every day. It's my mission to intercede for my family before the throne of grace, and I accept this responsibility with all my heart out of gratitude to God for all the blessings your grandfather and I were given during our time on earth. This is the way I express my love for all of you. It's a love that can never die—no matter what."

"Thank you for visiting me, Grandmother. I feel like I know you much better now, and I can see why your untimely death was such a devastating blow to our family."

"Death is always untimely, Dan. It's a reality that we must all face in our own lives and in the lives of those we love. In many ways, the measure of life, its true meaning and purpose, is shown in the way we deal with the mystery of death."

I can't remember a time when I have felt so thoroughly exhausted. I lie down on one of the benches and wrap my legs under me. I begin to pray, "God grant me the serenity ... ." My grandmother opens her purse and removes a small green pillow that I recognize from the love seat in my grandparents' bedroom on Claythorne Road. She places the pillow under my head and kisses me on the forehead. She is singing again. I fall into a deep sleep.

> *Each day is grey and dreary*
> *But the night is bright and cheery*
> *When the moon comes over the mountain*
> *I'll be alone with my memories of you.**

When I wake up in my hospital room sometime later, I'm shocked to see that my grandmother has not left me. She is curled up at the edge of the bed, sound asleep. No fear or anxiety trouble her now. She really is at peace. Please, God, may it always be so.

---

*When the Moon comes over the Mountain, by Howard Johnson, Harry M. Woods and Kathryn E. Smith was sung by my grandmother's favorite singer, Kate Smith, for more than 50 years in concert appearances, in films, and on radio and television.

CHAPTER 14
Helen

On the beach. My mother sits on a rock under a shady tree. This is a public beach in Naples, Florida, but it's small and it feels private—especially early in the morning. My mother is writing in a small notebook:

Waves
Majestically rise
Ruthlessly hurl
Greedily swirl
Always subside

The poem tells her story. It is who she is (or was during her 73 years of life), a restless wave gathering strength, rising up, crashing, receding and then regaining strength to rise, crash and recede all over again.

"Danny, dear," she calls out to me above the sound of the wind and waves. Her voice is dusky from years of smoking.

"I'm coming, Mom." This is one of those dreams where everything happens in slow motion, and it takes me forever to walk just a few steps across the footbridge from the street to the beach.

"Thank you for taking such good care of your father," she says. "That should have been my job, but I wouldn't have had the patience it requires. You children are so devoted to him. It's a great blessing, and it shows that as parents we did something right."

"Dad is easy to care for, Mom. He's always grateful and accepting—no matter what his troubles are."

"I know. We were married for 50 years. I always said he was my St. Joseph. He never gave up on me even when no one—especially me—would have blamed him for calling it quits."

Halfway through their marriage, my mother had a conversion experience. She joined Alcoholics Anonymous and began a program of recovery that was an inspiration to everyone who knew her. Sobriety gave her many gifts. She became an award-winning poet, a popular teacher of English, a friend to hundreds of women in need, and a devoted wife, mother and grandmother. I found her to be a good friend and confidant especially in her final years. She died of several contributing causes at the age of 73, but she remained grateful to the very end.

"Earlier this year, on your 61st wedding anniversary, Dad summed it all up very simply. 'We had a good life,' he told me. For him, the bad times have faded from sight, and the good times have become more real. He misses you terribly, but the memories of your years together are a source of joy and consolation for him."

"And what about you, dear? What do you remember most—the good times or the bad?"

"It's really hard to say, Mom. Over the years, everything mixes together. There's still a lot of pain in me just beneath the surface. It's the residue from the unhappiness of my teenage years. I've never been comfortable talking about those years. As you know from your own experience, Mom, growing up in an alcoholic home is always painful—and a source of inexplicable shame. But a lot of good people helped me channel the pain and resist the temptation to let it distort my attitude toward life."

"Do you know how much Jesus loves you, dear?"

I'm startled by the directness of her question. It makes me feel more than a little uncomfortable to have to talk about this now. I need to collect myself.

"I believe that God loves me, that Jesus died and rose for me, and that I'm destined to be happy with Him in heaven one day. But that's not what you're asking me, is it?"

"No, dear. I'm asking *if you have any idea how much Jesus loves you.*"

"No, Mom. I don't."

"I didn't either until my final years when I was in such terrible pain. I had to join my suffering with the agony of Jesus on the Cross. That gave me some comfort—and an insight into how much He loves me, but even then I had no real appreciation for the depth of His love."

"Pope Benedict says that heaven is like 'plunging into an ocean of infinite love.' Would that be an accurate description of how much Jesus loves us?"

"I think so. Look out into the Gulf. There is water as far as we can see, but it doesn't even begin to encompass this magnificent sea. God's love is infinite, but it's also very intimate and personal. He loves *me* unconditionally. And His love for *you* is immense and immeasurable. To get even a partial idea of how much Jesus loves us, we need to know Him personally and to love Him intimately through our goodness and generosity to others. That's a lesson I learned late in life. I pray it wasn't too late."

"Hope springs eternal," I say quoting one of her favorite poems.

The sun is so bright now that I realize we're not on the rocks any more. We're at the water's edge. This is the Atlantic Ocean, not the Gulf of Mexico, and the waves are much higher and more intense. I am no longer an adult. I'm only two years old, and I'm playing in the sand. My mother is distracted by my sister Anne, an infant lying on a beach blanket under an umbrella. I walk fearlessly into the ocean and, of course, lose my balance. The water overwhelms me. I begin to thrash my arms and legs wildly, doing myself no good at all. Then time slows down again, and I wait underwater for what seems like an eternity. It doesn't hurt at all. I'm just floating—and waiting for something to happen. Is this the end? Is my subconscious mind preparing me for death by taking me back to the very beginning of my life?

She is standing in front of me now. I can see her legs and her torso but not her face. She reaches down and lifts me out of the water into her arms. "Danny Demon," she says. "You scared the hell out of me."

I'm frightened, too, but I like being held by her and comforted. The sun burns my face and shoulders. Dream or no dream, I've had enough.

My mother puts me down—too soon, I think—and I'm lying on a beach blanket next to my sister. I can see my mother adjusting the beach umbrella so that we're lying in the shade. Mom lies down on the blanket in between the baby and me. Soon all three of us are asleep.

CHAPTER 15
On the road again:
Hope springs eternal

I begin to wake up and, for the first time, to move my arms and legs. Sharon and our five children are all in the hospital room with me. But others are here also. Am I the only one who can see them? This hospital room isn't big enough for them all, but here they are—my parents, my brothers and sisters, both sets of grandparents, all my aunts, uncles and cousins, hundreds of friends and coworkers—both living and deceased. They are all here, a communion of saints, calling me back to life, helping me to regain consciousness and, yes, to be reborn.

The great spiritual writer Romano Guardini once commented on Jesus' words: "Amen, amen I say to you, unless a man be born again of water and the Spirit, he cannot enter the Kingdom of God" (Jn 3:3-5). Monsignor Guardini writes, "How is such a thing possible? asks Nicodemus, and isn't his question our own—all the helplessness of it, the longing, the discontentment? There on the one hand stands Christ with his chosen ones radiating the beauty and plenitude of God; and here am I, entangled in myself, heavily forged to my own dark paltriness; how can I ever cross over to him? How, ever, escape from myself to share in all that he is? Jesus replies: You never will—alone."

I open my eyes and attempt to speak. "Don't try to talk," Sharon says. "There will be plenty of time for that later. Your brain damage is not permanent. With time, and a lot of physical therapy, you'll be as good as new."

Catherine wipes the tears from my eyes while Margaret checks my vital signs and my medication. Sharon straightens my sheets and adjusts my hospital gown.

"You'll have to go to a rehab facility before you can come home," Sharon says sensing my impatience to get out of here and go home with her.

113

I try to say—or even just mouth the words "I love you," but my lips won't move the way I want them to. There is so much I want to say—to everyone.

"Grandy wants to talk to you," Suzanne says. She holds the phone to my ear and the voice of my 87-year-old father comes through loud and clear.

"Say, Danny. Are you there?"

I can't respond, of course, but my Dad keeps talking.

"I wanted to come to Louisville to visit you in the hospital, but my doctor wouldn't let me. It's too soon after my gallbladder surgery. So I decided to pray my rosary for you every morning. They tell me it's working. You're getting better."

Suzanne hands the phone to her brother, Danny, who speaks for me. "Hi, Grandy. My Dad's doing fine. He'll have to do physical therapy, but we expect him to recover completely. When he does, I'll bring him down to Florida to see you."

A nurse comes in. It's time to change the IV and soon they'll be washing me and giving me a new gown.

"We're going down to the cafeteria," Sharon says. "We'll be back soon. Get some rest."

Mary kisses me on the forehead, and I can see she's been crying. If only I could speak! I touch her hand clumsily. It's the best I can do for now.

Archbishop Murphy loved to tell the story of his 60th birthday and his brother's Irish optimism. "Did you know that for every three years you've lived you have just one year left?" the archbishop's brother told him.

What does that mean for me, a 60-year-old man? Do I have twenty years left? The archbishop didn't live to be 80 and neither did most of the family members and friends who have visited me in my dreams since I arrived at this hospital. But whether I have many more years to live, or just a few, there's no question that the road ahead is much shorter than the one behind.

What I've learned during the past 60 years needs to be broadened and deepened and shared. This is the ultimate stewardship responsibility—to gather the experiences of an entire lifetime, to nurture and develop them, and to share them unselfishly with others.

Whatever time is left on the road ahead, the folks who visited me when I was on the edge, in the borderland between living and dying, have clearly shown me what I need to do to be ready for the particular judgment I'll receive when I die.

I need to:
- pay more attention to Sharon and our family,
- surrender,
- be grateful,
- be humble,
- achieve some mastery over my emotions and my "unruly desires,"
- not take myself so damned seriously,
- forgive even when I can't forget, and
- find some measure of peace and joy, through knowing, loving, and serving Jesus.

One day at a time.

I've learned that we have gratitude, not certainty. And that we have humor, the only cure for madness. Above all, I know now, as never before, that hope springs eternal.

The room is empty now, and I am alone.

Or am I?

In the corner by the window I think I see a large man standing in the shadows. It looks like the man who resembles my grandfather's friend Charlie (aka Thursday). Am I dreaming again? I kick my legs—and the sheets fall off the bed onto the floor. I am definitely not dreaming.

"You are not alone," he whispers. "Care to join me in a glass of milk punch?"

Author's note

Alcoholism has been part of my family (on all sides) since before anyone can remember. In fact, most of the people portrayed in this book suffered from the effects of alcoholism either in their personal lives or in the lives of their families or close friends. Alcoholism is a family disease. Because alcoholism causes its victims to suffer mentally, emotionally and spiritually—as well as physically—relationships between the alcoholic and his/her spouse, children and even siblings or other extended family members become distorted and confused. It is not unusual for alcoholic families to experience all kinds of dysfunctions and for abusive, alcoholic behavior to be passed on from generation to generation.

By the grace of God, Alcoholics Anonymous became part of our family's story more than 50 years ago. As a result, dozens of my family members have been saved years of heartache and misery. Now the principles of AA, a program of recovery that offers experience, strength and hope to all who suffer from the ravages of alcoholism, is being handed-on to members of my family (on all sides). Please, God, may it always be so.

In this book, my friend DJ Champion is the voice of AA. I have broken his anonymity with the blessing of his wife, Sandy, and with the certain knowledge, based on our many years of friendship, that he wouldn't have had it any other way.

Acknowledgments

I would like to thank the following people for their assistance in writing this book:

My wife, Sharon Conway, who served as a faithful companion and as chief medical advisor in this bold new adventure in my career as a writer.

My cousin Ann Conley Erickson, who was the first person I talked to about the idea for this book and who told me to "hang in there" until the revision process, which she described as "a kind of Möbius strip," was completed.

My friend, and former student, Ralph Vince, who challenged me (not always successfully) to move beyond the familiar.

My friend Sandra Goltz Champion, who provided insights (and stories) about DJ, the man she loves still.

My friend and editor Bill Bruns, who encouraged me even as he questioned and corrected me.

My friend and former professor Gill Ring who taught me by his words and his example how to think and live as a man.

My aunt and literary advisor Linda Glick Conway, who says she is "not a Conway by blood," but who certainly is a Conway.

My Uncles Tim, Bud, Bill and Gerry Conway who shared with me their memories of, and deep love for, the grandmother I never knew, Margaret Nelson Conway.

And my father, Jack Conway, who inspired me (as he always does) by his enthusiasm for life and his patient acceptance of life's many burdens.